Higher
Art & Design

First exam published in 2003.

Published by Leckie & Leckie Ltd, 3rd Floor, 4 Queen Street, Edinburgh EH2 1JE

tel: 0131 220 6831 fax: 0131 225 9987 enquiries@leckieandleckie.co.uk www.leckieandleckie.co.uk

ISBN 1-84372-433-2   ISBN-13 978-1-84372-433-9

A CIP Catalogue record for this book is available from the British Library.

Printed in Scotland by Scotprint.

Leckie & Leckie is a division of Granada Learning Limited.

Leckie & Leckie is grateful to the copyright holders, as credited at the back of the book, for permission to use their material. Every effort has been made to trace the copyright holders and to obtain their permission for the use of copyright material. Leckie & Leckie will gladly receive information enabling them to rectify any error or omission in subsequent editions.

[BLANK PAGE]

X003/301

NATIONAL
QUALIFICATIONS
2003

ART AND DESIGN
HIGHER
Paper 1
Practical Assignment

The Practical Examinations for the 2003 examination diet may take place at the centre's discretion on the most convenient date in the period from Monday 28 April until Friday 9 May inclusive.

Time allowed: 3 hours

50 marks are assigned to this paper.

Maximum sizes: Two-dimensional work: A2.
                   Three-dimensional work: 30 cm in greatest dimension.

Any medium except oil paint may be used.

SCOTTISH
QUALIFICATIONS
AUTHORITY

GENERAL INSTRUCTIONS

Base your work for the Practical Assignment on your Expressive Activity folio **or** your Design Activity folio.

In the examination room you may refer to:

• Design **or** Expressive Folio of work

• Practical Assignment Form

You may use any three-dimensional source materials identified in the folio you have selected.

You will be allowed up to 20 minutes after the examination to assemble your work on the maximum number of sheets (2 × A2 sheets).

This extension time is not to be used for producing examination work.

Note: Mechanical reproductions of drawings and/or photographs copied from your folio by means such as TRACING, LIGHT BOXES and PHOTOCOPYING **will not be permitted during the examination**. This exclusion also includes images and/or information copied from folios and stored on disk, CD or digital camera.

Select **either** SECTION A **or** SECTION B.

SECTION A

Expressive Activity

Task

You should produce practical work which demonstrates your ability to develop and/or refine work carried out in your Expressive folio. This could take the form of new and further developments from your stimulus and might include extending ideas leading to alternative outcome(s) not fully explored within the work of your folio.

Remember that work produced for this Assignment should relate directly to your EXPRESSIVE folio theme and must develop, not copy, work already done. Further investigative work, such as analytical drawing, is not appropriate in this Assignment.

The following suggestions are provided to help you get started:

• produce work based on the stimulus or sources used by you but not fully explored in the work of your Expressive folio

• produce work which emphasises a different style of approach to your chosen theme.

Work should be on a maximum of **two** A2 sheets or equivalent three-dimensional work. You may use any suitable media, materials or process.

SECTION B

Design Activity

Task

You should produce practical work which demonstrates an alternative approach or approaches to work carried out in your Design folio. This could take the form of new and further developments from your brief and might include extending Design ideas not fully explored within the work of your folio.

Remember that work produced for this Assignment should relate to your DESIGN brief and design folio and must develop, not copy, work already done. Further investigative work, such as analytical drawing, is not appropriate in this Assignment.

The following suggestions are provided to help you get started:

- develop design ideas which you considered but did not fully explore in the work of your Design folio

- reconsider your solution and suggest further modifications and/or changes to improve it.

Work should be on a maximum of **two** A2 sheets or equivalent three-dimensional work. You may use any suitable media, materials or process.

[END OF QUESTION PAPER]

[BLANK PAGE]

X003/302

| NATIONAL QUALIFICATIONS 2003 | THURSDAY, 5 JUNE 1.00 PM – 3.00 PM | ART AND DESIGN HIGHER Paper 2 |

There are **two** sections to this paper, Section 1—Art Studies; and Section 2—Design Studies. Each section is worth 40 marks.

Candidates should attempt questions as follows:

In SECTION 1 answer **ONE full question** (parts *(a)* and *(b)*) and **ONE part *(a)* only** of any other question

and

In SECTION 2 answer **ONE full question** (parts *(a)* and *(b)*) and **ONE part *(a)* only** of any other question.

You may use sketches to illustrate your answers.

SCOTTISH
QUALIFICATIONS
AUTHORITY ©

SECTION 1—ART STUDIES

Instructions

Answer **ONE full question** (parts (*a*) and (*b*)), and **ONE part (*a*) only** of any other question.

John Everett Millais   *The Bridesmaid* (1851) oil on panel (27·9 × 20·3 cm)

1.   Portraiture

Marks

(*a*)   Discuss the composition of this portrait.   Comment on the use of visual elements and media handling.   In your opinion, how successfully has the artist communicated his thoughts about the bridesmaid?   **10**

(*b*)   Discuss examples of portraiture by **two** artists from different movements or periods.   Comment on their choice of subjects and working methods.   To what extent has their work influenced other artists?   **20**

SECTION 1—ART STUDIES (continued)

Joyce Cairns   *Last Supper* (1989) oil on board (205·8 × 235·2 cm)

2. Figure Composition

Marks

(*a*) Discuss the composition of this painting. Comment on **at least two** of the following:

colour;   line;   distortion;   perspective.

In what way does the title affect your interpretation of this work?

10

(*b*) Discuss examples of figure composition by **two** artists from different movements or periods. Comment on the differences and/or similarities in their approaches and working methods. Explain why you consider them to be important artists.

20

[Turn over

SECTION 1—ART STUDIES (continued)

Meret Oppenheim   *Object: Breakfast in Fur* (1936) cup, saucer and spoon covered with fur

Marks

3.   Still Life

(*a*)   Discuss the choice of materials and method used by the artist to create this still life. How do you think it challenges traditional approaches to still life? What is your personal opinion of the piece?

10

(*b*)   Compare examples of still life by **two** artists from different movements or periods. Discuss the artists' particular contribution to still life and comment on their choice of subject matter, styles and working methods.

20

SECTION 1—ART STUDIES (continued)

J.M.W. Turner   *Norham Castle, Sunrise* (1840–45) oil on canvas (90·8 × 121·9 cm)
© Tate, London 2003

4. Natural Environment

Marks

(*a*)   Discuss the methods used by Turner to produce this response to nature. In doing so, comment on his use of colour, shape and media handling. How successful do you think Turner has been in capturing the atmosphere of a particular moment?

10

(*b*)   Discuss examples of work by **two** artists from different movements or periods who have been inspired by the natural environment. What similarities exist in their work and in which ways do they differ? Explain why you consider them to be important artists.

20

[Turn over

SECTION 1—ART STUDIES (continued)

L.S. Lowry   *A Manufacturing Town* (1922) oil on board (43·2 × 53·3 cm)

5.   Built Environment

Marks

(*a*)   How successful do you think Lowry has been in communicating the industrial nature of this town to the viewer? In your response comment on **at least two** of the following:

colour;   tone;   shape;   perspective.

10

(*b*)   Discuss examples of work, within this theme, by **two** artists from different movements or periods. Comment on their choice of subject matter and treatment of it. Explain why you consider these artists to be influential.

20

SECTION 1—ART STUDIES (continued)

Marc Chagall *I and the Village* (1911) oil on canvas (192·1 × 151·4 cm)

6. Fantasy and Imagination

Marks

(a) This painting is based on the artist's memories of childhood. Discuss the methods used by the artist to create this image which conveys his personal experience. Briefly give your opinion of the painting. **10**

(b) Select **two** artists from different movements or periods whose work is based on fantasy and imagination. Discuss examples of their work and explain the methods used to communicate their ideas. Why do you consider the artists you have selected to be important contributors to this theme? **20**

[Turn over

SECTION 2—DESIGN STUDIES

Instructions

Answer **ONE full question** (parts (*a*) and (*b*)), and **ONE part (*a*) only** of any other question.

Poster design for International Business Machines (IBM), by Paul Rand (1981)

7. Graphic Design

Marks

(*a*) Identify the key design features of this poster. What message does it communicate, and how well does it succeed? Justify your answer.

10

(*b*) Select **two** designers from different periods or working in different styles. Discuss examples of their graphic designs that incorporate text and/or imagery in the layout. How has the work of these designers contributed to the communication of marketing ideas and/or corporate identity?

20

SECTION 2—DESIGN STUDIES (continued)

Detail of camera lens.

Mobile phone with Multimedia Messaging Service (MMS) and built-in camera.
Model 7250 by Nokia (2003).

Marks

8. Product Design

(*a*) Discuss the strengths and weaknesses of this multi-functional communication
tool. In your response refer to **at least two** of the following:

style; function; safety and security; technology; materials;

cultural trends.   **10**

(*b*) Select **two** product designers working in different periods or styles. Comment
on the ways that their designs have improved the quality of everyday life. Refer
to specific examples in your answer.   **20**

[Turn over

SECTION 2—DESIGN STUDIES (continued)

Chiat Day Offices, New York City, designed by Gaetano Pesce (1993–96)

9. Interior Design

Marks

(a) How does this interior differ from a typical office environment? Which key design elements contribute to its effectiveness as a workspace? Do you think the designer has created a successful solution? Justify your answer.

10

(b) Compare **two** interior designers from different periods or who work in contrasting styles. Highlight the main features of their work and state why they are considered to be important designers.

20

SECTION 2—DESIGN STUDIES (continued)

North facing facade.

Main entrance, Renfrew Street.

Glasgow School of Art, designed by Charles Rennie Mackintosh (1897/1909)

10. Environmental/Architectural Design

Marks

(*a*) What are the key features of this architectural design that contribute to its distinctive appearance? Identify what you think the architect's primary design considerations would have been in relation to the function of this building. Give reasons in support of your answer.

10

(*b*) Select **two** architects or environmental designers from different periods or who work in highly contrasting styles. Discuss the characteristics of their work and show, with reference to materials, form and innovation, why they are important figures in this area of design.

20

[Turn over

SECTION 2—DESIGN STUDIES (continued)

Two examples of Brooches of Coloured Tears designed by Wendy Ramshaw (1998).
Each brooch is 27 cm × 7 cm and made of 18ct gold with multi-coloured stones.

11. Jewellery Design

Marks

(a) How well does Wendy Ramshaw's design capture the theme? Refer to her use of materials, colour, shape and form in your answer. In what circumstances might this jewellery be worn? Give reasons.

10

(b) "Influences and visual stimuli are highly important factors in the development of exciting jewellery ideas." Select **two** jewellery designers, who work in different periods or styles, and discuss this statement in relation to their work. Why are they regarded as important designers?

20

SECTION 2—DESIGN STUDIES (continued)

Evening Coat with Embroidery designed by Elsa Schiaparelli (1937)

12. Textile Design

Marks

(a) What important design issues were considered in the development of this fashion item? In your response refer to **at least two** of the following:

colour; texture; ambiguity; materials; form; humour.

What is your opinion of this coat?

10

(b) Fashion and textile designers are required to produce ideas for different target markets. Select **two** fashion/textile designers working in different periods or styles. Show, with reference to examples of their work, how they have responded to this challenge. Why are they important designers?

20

[END OF QUESTION PAPER]

[BLANK PAGE]

2004 | Higher

[BLANK PAGE]

X003/301

NATIONAL
QUALIFICATIONS
2004

ART AND DESIGN
HIGHER
Paper 1
Practical Assignment

The Practical Examinations for the 2004 examination diet may take place at the centre's discretion on the most convenient date in the period from Monday 26 April until Friday 7 May inclusive.

Time allowed: 3 hours

50 marks are assigned to this paper.

Maximum sizes: Two-dimensional work: A2.
                       Three-dimensional work: 30 cm in greatest dimension.

Any medium except oil paint may be used.

SCOTTISH
QUALIFICATIONS
AUTHORITY

GENERAL INSTRUCTIONS

Base your work for the Practical Assignment on your Expressive Activity folio **or** your Design Activity folio.

In the examination room you may refer to:

• Design **or** Expressive Folio of work

• Practical Assignment Form

You may use any three-dimensional source materials identified in the folio you have selected.

You will be allowed up to 20 minutes after the examination to assemble your work on the maximum number of sheets (2 ↔ A2 sheets).

This extension time is not to be used for producing examination work.

Note: Copying of drawings and/or photographs from your folio by means such as TRACING, LIGHT BOXES, DIGITAL CAMERAS and PHOTOCOPYING **will not be permitted during the examination**. This exclusion also includes images and/or information copied from folios and stored on disk and/or CD.

Select **either** SECTION A **or** SECTION B.

SECTION A

Expressive Activity

Task

You should produce practical work which demonstrates your ability to develop and/or refine work carried out in your Expressive folio. This could take the form of new and further developments from your stimulus and might include extending ideas leading to alternative outcome(s) not fully explored within the work of your folio.

Remember that work produced for this Assignment should relate directly to your EXPRESSIVE folio theme and must develop, not copy, work already done. Further investigative work, such as analytical drawing, is not appropriate in this Assignment.

The following suggestions are provided to help you get started:

• produce work based on the stimulus or sources used by you but not fully explored in the work of your Expressive folio

• produce work which emphasises a different style or approach to your chosen theme.

Work should be on a maximum of **two** A2 sheets or equivalent three-dimensional work. You may use any suitable media, materials or process.

SECTION B

Design Activity

Task

You should produce practical work which demonstrates an alternative approach or approaches to work carried out in your Design folio. This could take the form of new and further developments from your brief and might include extending Design ideas not fully explored within the work of your folio.

Remember that work produced for this Assignment should relate to your DESIGN brief and design folio and must develop, not copy, work already done. Further investigative work, such as analytical drawing, is not appropriate in this Assignment.

The following suggestions are provided to help you get started:

• develop design ideas which you considered but did not fully explore in the work of your Design folio

• reconsider your solution and suggest further modifications and/or changes to improve it.

Work should be on a maximum of **two** A2 sheets or equivalent three-dimensional work. You may use any suitable media, materials or process.

[END OF QUESTION PAPER]

[BLANK PAGE]

X003/302

NATIONAL QUALIFICATIONS 2004	WEDNESDAY, 2 JUNE 1.00PM – 3.00PM	ART AND DESIGN HIGHER Paper 2

There are **two** sections to this paper, Section 1—Art Studies; and Section 2—Design Studies.

Each section is worth 40 marks.

Candidates should attempt questions as follows:

In SECTION 1 answer **ONE full question** (parts (a) and (b)) and **ONE part (a) only** of any other question

and

In SECTION 2 answer **ONE full question** (parts (a) and (b)) and **ONE part (a) only** of any other question.

You may use sketches to illustrate your answers.

SCOTTISH
QUALIFICATIONS
AUTHORITY

SECTION 1—ART STUDIES

Instructions

Answer **ONE full question**, (parts (*a*) and (*b*)), and **ONE part (*a*) only** of any other question.

Lucian Freud   *Interior at Paddington* (1951) oil on canvas (152·4 × 114·3 cm)

Marks

1.   Portraiture

(*a*)   What is the artist communicating to us in this painting of his friend? In your answer refer to the artist's use of visual elements and **at least two** of the following:

pose,   composition,   detail,   setting.   **10**

(*b*)   Compare **two** artists from different movements or periods whose work in portraiture is contrasting in style. Discuss the main characteristics of their work and explain why you consider them to be important artists in the history of portraiture.

20

SECTION 1—ART STUDIES (continued)

Jean Francois Millet   *The Woodsawyers* (1850–52) oil on canvas (57 × 81 cm)

Marks

2.   Figure Composition

(a)   Discuss the composition of this painting. Comment on the methods used by the artist to communicate dramatic atmosphere and intense activity. What is your opinion of the painting?

10

(b)   Compare examples of figure composition by **two** artists from different movements or periods. Discuss the methods used by the artists to communicate their ideas. Explain why the artists are considered to be important contributors to the art of figure composition.

20

[Turn over

SECTION 1—ART STUDIES (continued)

Elizabeth Blackadder *White Anemones* (1983) watercolour (55·8 × 78·8 cm)

Marks

3. Still Life

(a) Discuss the composition of this painting. Comment on **two** of the following:

use of space, subject matter, media handling, use of visual elements.

What is your opinion of this still life painting? **10**

(b) Compare an example of still life by **two** artists from different movements or periods. In doing so, explain:

how typical your chosen examples are of their associated movements.

OR

how influential each artist has been in the development of still life. **20**

SECTION 1—ART STUDIES (continued)

Claude Monet   *Poplars in the Sun* (1891) oil on canvas (88·3 × 92·7 cm)

Marks

4. Natural Environment

(a) Discuss Monet's choice of subject matter and explain the methods used by him to communicate the beauty of the scene. In your opinion, how successful has Monet been in achieving this? **10**

(b) Discuss examples by **two** artists from different movements or periods whose work is a response to the natural environment. Comment on the working methods used by the artists. Explain why you consider them to be important artists. **20**

[Turn over

SECTION 1—ART STUDIES (continued)

Rachel Whiteread   *Untitled (House)* (1993) concrete and plaster (10 m high approx)

Marks

5.   **Built Environment**

This sculpture was made by taking casts, in plaster and concrete, from a real house.

(*a*)   Discuss the sculptor's choice of subject matter and her treatment of it. What effects have her working methods had on the visual impact of this piece? What is your opinion of this "inside out" sculpture?   **10**

(*b*)   Select **two** artists from different movements or periods whose work is based on the built environment. Discuss examples of their work commenting upon their choice of subject matter and working methods. To what extent did these artists influence others?   **20**

SECTION 1—ART STUDIES (continued)

Edward Burra   *Storm in the Jungle* (1931) watercolour (55·4 × 67·9 cm)

Marks

6.   Fantasy and Imagination

(*a*)   Discuss the content and composition of this painting.   Comment on the artist's use of colour, line and pattern.   What is your personal interpretation of the painting?   **10**

(*b*)   Compare examples of work by **two** important artists from different movements or periods.   Discuss the methods used by the artists to communicate their ideas on the theme of fantasy and imagination.   Explain why you consider the examples to be typical of the artists' styles.   **20**

[Turn over

SECTION 2—DESIGN STUDIES

Instructions

Answer **ONE full question**, (parts (*a*) and (*b*)), and **ONE part (*a*) only** of any other question.

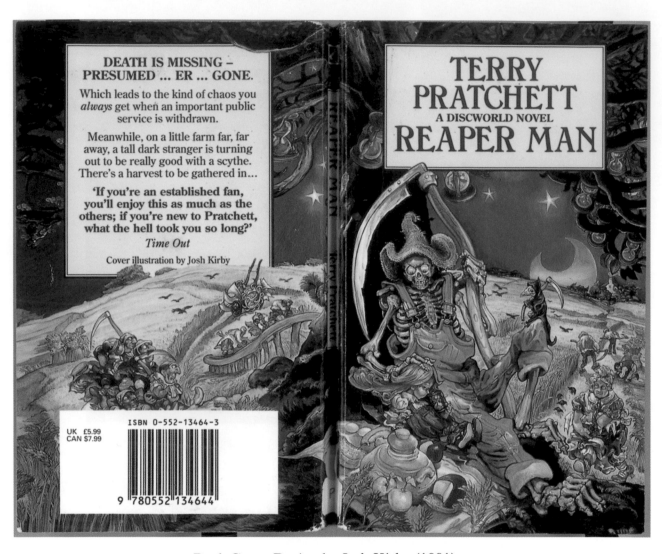

Book Cover Design by Josh Kirby (1991)

Marks

7. Graphic Design

(*a*) It is often said that you cannot judge a book by its cover. How does this design contribute to the marketing of the book? Refer to **at least two** of the following in your answer:

imagery, layout, text, target market, colour.

Do you think it is a successful design? Give reasons. **10**

(*b*) Select **two** graphic designers from different periods or whose styles are contrasting. With reference to specific examples of their work, explain how they communicate their ideas effectively to a wide audience. Why are they considered to be important graphic designers? **20**

SECTION 2—DESIGN STUDIES (continued)

Swiss Army Knife developed from original design by Carl and Victoria Elsener (1891).
Design pictured above—stainless steel and plastic (actual size)

Marks

8. Product Design

(*a*) Discuss the strengths and weaknesses of this multi-functional tool kit design. Why do you think it is still a successful product today? **10**

(*b*) Choose **two** product designers working in different periods or styles. Discuss how their ideas have contributed to the way we live our lives. Refer to specific examples of their work in your answer. Why are they important designers? **20**

SECTION 2—DESIGN STUDIES (continued)

JetBlue Airways—Airbus A320–232 (2001)

Marks

9. Interior Design

(*a*) What important design issues did the designer have to consider in the interior of this aircraft? How successful is the design solution? Give reasons for your answer.

10

(*b*) Select **two** interior designers who have worked in contrasting ways or are from different periods. Show why they are important figures in the development of design. Discuss their unique and distinctive approach to the design of interior spaces. You should refer, in some detail, to a typical example by each designer.

20

The Crown Street Housing Regeneration Project—Gorbals, Glasgow 2002
Architect—Piers Gough

Marks

10. Environmental/Architectural Design

(a) Comment on the effectiveness of this urban housing redevelopment. In your answer, refer to the use of materials, the building's appearance, and the use of artwork. How do you think this kind of environmental design might improve the life of the community?

10

(b) Discuss examples of environmental design/architecture by **two** designers/ architects working in different periods or in contrasting styles. With reference to the important characteristics of their work, comment on their contribution to the built environment of today.

20

SECTION 2—DESIGN STUDIES (continued)

Belt Buckle in silver and enamel by Jessie M. King (1906)

Marks

11. Jewellery Design

(a) What influences do you think have inspired this design? Compare it with contemporary buckles. In what ways can this buckle be justified as a piece of jewellery?

10

(b) Select **two** jewellery designers working in different periods or whose approaches to design are contrasting. With reference to examples of their work, discuss why they are highly respected designers. Refer to **at least two** of the following in support of your answer:

originality, range of work, influences, processes, function, style.

20

Hand-knit Jacket and Sweater, Fringed Skirt by Issey Miyake (1983)

Marks

12. Textile Design

(*a*) Comment on Issey Miyake's use of textures, pattern and techniques in this outfit. How does the design relate to the body and what do you think Miyake was trying to achieve here? What is your opinion of this outfit?

10

(*b*) Fashion/textile designers are constantly challenged to find new ways to create clothing and fabrics. Choose **two** important designers working in different periods or styles who are recognised for their contribution in either field. With reference to examples of their work, discuss their working methods and approaches to design.

20

[END OF QUESTION PAPER]

[BLANK PAGE]

2005 | Higher

[BLANK PAGE]

X003/301

NATIONAL
QUALIFICATIONS
2005

ART AND DESIGN
HIGHER
Paper 1
Practical Assignment

The Practical Examinations for the 2005 examination diet may take place at the centre's discretion on the most convenient date in the period from Monday 25 April until Friday 6 May inclusive.

Time allowed: 3 hours

50 marks are assigned to this paper.

Maximum sizes: Two-dimensional work: A2.
                      Three-dimensional work: 30 cm in greatest dimension.

Any medium except oil paint may be used.

SCOTTISH
QUALIFICATIONS
AUTHORITY

©

GENERAL INSTRUCTIONS

Base your work for the Practical Assignment on your Expressive Activity folio **or** your Design Activity folio.

In the examination room you may refer to:

• Design **or** Expressive Folio of work

• Practical Assignment Form

You may use any three-dimensional source materials identified in the folio you have selected.

You will be allowed up to 20 minutes after the examination to assemble your work on the maximum number of sheets (2 × A2 sheets).

This extension time is not to be used for producing examination work.

Note: Copying of drawings and/or photographs from your folio by means such as TRACING, LIGHT BOXES, DIGITAL CAMERAS and PHOTOCOPYING **will not be permitted during the examination**. This exclusion also includes images and/or information copied from folios and stored on disk and/or CD.

Select **either** SECTION A **or** SECTION B.

SECTION A

Expressive Activity

Task

You should produce practical work which demonstrates your ability to develop and/or refine work carried out in your Expressive folio. This could take the form of new and further developments from your stimulus and might include extending ideas leading to alternative outcome(s) not fully explored within the work of your folio.

Remember that work produced for this Assignment should relate directly to your EXPRESSIVE folio theme and must develop, not copy, work already done. Further investigative work, such as analytical drawing, is not appropriate in this Assignment.

The following suggestions are provided to help you get started:

• produce work based on the stimulus or sources used by you but not fully explored in the work of your Expressive folio

• produce work which emphasises a different style or approach to your chosen theme.

Work should be on a maximum of **two** A2 sheets or equivalent three-dimensional work. You may use any suitable media, materials or process.

SECTION B

Design Activity

Task

You should produce practical work which demonstrates an alternative approach or approaches to work carried out in your Design folio. This could take the form of new and further developments from your brief and might include extending Design ideas not fully explored within the work of your folio.

Remember that work produced for this Assignment should relate to your DESIGN brief and design folio and must develop, not copy, work already done. Further investigative work, such as analytical drawing, is not appropriate in this Assignment.

The following suggestions are provided to help you get started:

• develop design ideas which you considered but did not fully explore in the work of your Design folio

• reconsider your solution and suggest further modifications and/or changes to improve it.

Work should be on a maximum of **two** A2 sheets or equivalent three-dimensional work. You may use any suitable media, materials or process.

[END OF QUESTION PAPER]

[BLANK PAGE]

X003/302

NATIONAL
QUALIFICATIONS
2005

TUESDAY, 31 MAY
1.00PM – 3.00PM

ART AND DESIGN
HIGHER
Paper 2

There are **two** sections to this paper, Section 1—Art Studies; and Section 2—Design Studies.

Each section is worth 40 marks.

Candidates should attempt questions as follows:

In SECTION 1 answer **ONE full question** (parts (a) and (b)) and **ONE part (a) only** of any other question

and

In SECTION 2 answer **ONE full question** (parts (a) and (b)) and **ONE part (a) only** of any other question.

You may use sketches to illustrate your answers.

SCOTTISH
QUALIFICATIONS
AUTHORITY

SECTION 1—ART STUDIES

Instructions

Answer **ONE full question**, (parts (*a*) and (*b*)), and **ONE part (*a*) only** of any other question.

Frida Kahlo   *Diego on My Mind (Self-Portrait as Tehuana[1] Indian)* (1943)
oil on canvas (75 × 59·7 cm)

[1]*Tehuana*—a native of a southern region of Mexico

1. **Portraiture**   *Marks*

(*a*) Explain to what extent you consider this to be an accurate self portrait of the artist or an example of imaginative painting. Refer to the artist's use of visual elements and her symbolic use of images.   **10**

(*b*) Referring to examples of portraiture by **two** artists from different movements or periods, explain why you consider the works to be successful. How important are these artists in the development of portraiture?   **20**

SECTION 1—ART STUDIES (continued)

Paula Rego   *The Dance* (1988) acrylic on paper on canvas (213·4 × 274·3 cm)

Marks

2.   Figure Composition

(*a*)   Discuss the composition of this painting. Comment on the methods used by the artist to create strong visual impact. What is your opinion of the painting?   **10**

(*b*)   Discuss examples of figure composition by **two** artists from different movements or periods. Outline the methods used by the artists to create their work. Explain to what extent the examples are typical of their style or associated movement.   **20**

[Turn over

SECTION 1—ART STUDIES (continued)

Henri Fantin-Latour   *Still Life with Vase of Hydrangeas and Ranunculus* (1866)
oil on canvas (73 × 59·6 cm)

Marks

3. Still Life

(*a*) Analyse this painting in terms of the artist's choice of subject matter. Refer to composition, media handling and his use of visual elements. What is your opinion of this painting? **10**

(*b*) Select **two** artists from different movements or periods. Referring to at least one example by each of them, explain differences and/or similarities in their approach to still life. To what extent are the artists influential in the development of still life? **20**

SECTION 1—ART STUDIES (continued)

Raoul Dufy   *The Wheatfield* (1929) oil on canvas (130 × 162 cm)

Marks

4. Natural Environment

(a) Discuss the methods used by Dufy to create depth and atmosphere in this painting. Refer to his use of visual elements and painting style. What is your opinion of this painting? **10**

(b) Select **two** artists from different movements or periods whose works respond to the natural environment. Discuss what each artist has communicated to you about the environment. Comment on their choice of subject matter and their working methods. Why are they considered to be important artists? **20**

[Turn over

SECTION 1—ART STUDIES (continued)

Lyonel Feininger   *Market Church at Evening* (1930) oil on canvas (102 × 80·5 cm)

Marks

5. Built Environment

(*a*) Discuss the artist's treatment of this subject.   Comment on his use of line, colour and tone.   Identify aspects of the painting you admire and/or those you consider to be less successful. In doing so, give reasons.   **10**

(*b*) Referring to the work of **two** artists from different movements or periods discuss their treatment of the built environment. Comment on their choice of subject matter and working methods. To what extent is their work typical of their associated movements or styles?   **20**

SECTION 1—ART STUDIES (continued)

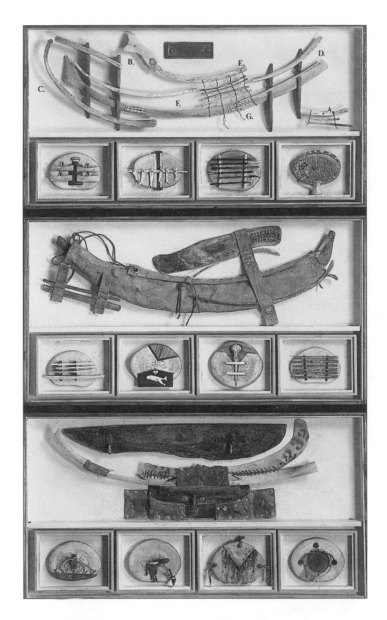

Will Maclean   *Leviathan*[1] *Elegy*[2] (1982)
painted whalebone and found objects[3] (203 × 137 × 10 cm)

[1] *Leviathan*—something of enormous size and power

[2] *Elegy*—a sorrowful poem

[3] This work is constructed from found, carved and painted objects assembled in three boxes.

Marks

6.   Fantasy and Imagination

(a)   Discuss the content of this work and the artist's method of presenting it. Comment on at least **two** of the following:

form,   scale,   materials,   colour,   composition.

What, in your opinion, is the artist communicating to us in this piece?   **10**

(b)   Discuss examples by **two** artists from different movements or periods whose work is within the theme of fantasy and imagination.   Comment on the sources of inspiration and methods used by the artists to produce their work. Explain why these artists are considered to be important.   **20**

Instructions

Answer **ONE full question**, (parts (*a*) and (*b*)), and **ONE part (*a*) only** of any other question.

Nihil[1]—CD design for band called KMFDM (1995)
designed by Francesca Sundsten and Chris Zander for Wax Trax!/TVT Records

[1]*Nihil*—nothingness

7. Graphic Design

Marks

(*a*) Discuss this example of graphic design by referring to imagery, colour and type. What do you think the design communicates about the band, the music and the target market?

10

(*b*) Select **two** graphic designers whose work is from different periods or in different styles. Choose examples of work by these designers and show how their methods of communication differ, by referring to at least **two** of the following:

image,   text,   layout,   visual impact,   technology.

20

Explain why they are considered to be important graphic designers.

SECTION 2—DESIGN STUDIES (continued)

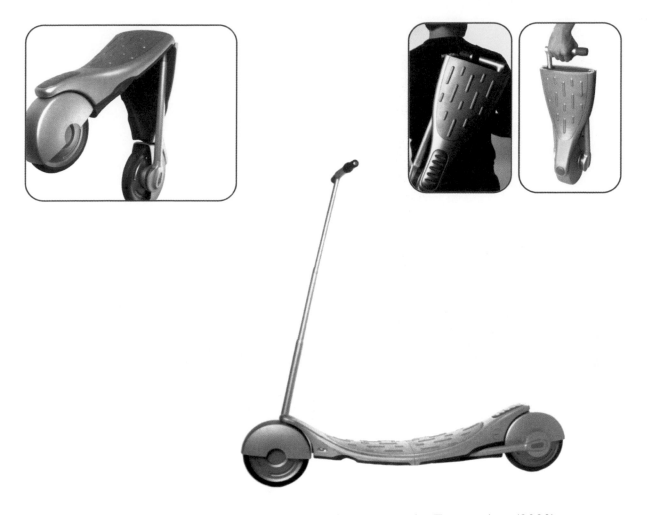

Scoot foldable, carbon fibre and aluminium scooter by Fuseproject (2000)

The scooter is propelled by hydrogen fuel without harming the environment.

Marks

8.   Product Design

(a)   What, in your opinion, are the main attractions and/or disadvantages of this scooter design? Discuss fully, giving reasons for your conclusions.   **10**

(b)   Product designers are constantly trying to meet the demands of an ever-changing market place. Choose **two** product designers, working in different periods or styles, who have demonstrated that they have met this challenge. Referring to specific examples of their work, explain why they are important designers.   **20**

[Turn over

SECTION 2—DESIGN STUDIES (continued)

Domestic Interior, Standen, Sussex, England designed by Philip Webb (1892–94)

Marks

9. Interior Design

(*a*) Discuss the elements used by the designer to create this interior typical of the period. What are your views of his use of space and furnishings? How does the interior differ from a living/sitting room of today?

10

(*b*) Select **two** interior designers who work in different periods or in contrasting styles. Refer to examples of their work, and show how *materials*, *working methods* and *changing fashions* have enabled them to develop new and exciting interior spaces. Explain why they are regarded as influential designers.

20

SECTION 2—DESIGN STUDIES (continued)

Clear Channel Adshel—Enthoven Line Trainshelter (with public phone) (circa 2000)
designed by Enthoven Associates

Marks

10. Environmental/Architectural Design

(*a*) Highlight the main issues to be considered by the designer(s) in the development of this "street design". How successful is the design? Give reasons for your views.

10

(*b*) Select **two** environmental/architectural designers who work in different periods or whose styles are contrasting.

Compare and contrast typical work by each of them by referring to the following:

materials, working methods, influences, aesthetics.

Why are they important designers?

20

[Turn over

SECTION 2—DESIGN STUDIES (continued)

Backpiece and Handpiece in white pewter and buffalo leather by Articular (1996)

Marks

11. Jewellery Design

(*a*) What do you think the design team is communicating through these jewellery designs? How practical are these ideas and when might they be worn? What are your personal thoughts about this approach to jewellery design? **10**

(*b*) Select **two** jewellery designers who work in contrasting styles or are from different periods. Discuss why they are regarded as innovative and influential designers by referring to at least **two** of the following:

function,   use of materials,   techniques,   aesthetics,   technology.

Refer to examples of their work in your answer. **20**

SECTION 2—DESIGN STUDIES (continued)

Personal Protection Unit designed by Edward Harber (2003)

This suit is made from Kevlar, a strong, synthetic, protective material.

Marks

12. Textile Design

(a) Discuss this motorcycle suit by referring to the key design issues considered by the designer. Can it be justified as a fashion item? Give reasons for your answer.

10

(b) Choose **two** fashion/textile designers whose styles are contrasting or who work in different periods. With reference to specific examples of their work, show how their distinctive approach to design has made them important and influential figures in their field.

20

[*END OF QUESTION PAPER*]

[BLANK PAGE]

2006 | Higher

[BLANK PAGE]

X003/301

NATIONAL
QUALIFICATIONS
2006

ART AND DESIGN
HIGHER
Paper 1
Practical Assignment

The Practical Examinations for the 2006 examination diet may take place at the centre's discretion on the most convenient date in the period from Monday 24 April until Friday 5 May inclusive.

Time allowed: 3 hours

50 marks are assigned to this paper.

Maximum sizes: Two-dimensional work: A2.
Three-dimensional work: 30 cm in greatest dimension.

Any medium except oil paint may be used.

SCOTTISH
QUALIFICATIONS
AUTHORITY

GENERAL INSTRUCTIONS

Base your work for the Practical Assignment on your Expressive Activity folio **or** your Design Activity folio.

In the examination room you may refer to your:

- Design **or** Expressive Folio of work

- Practical Assignment Form

You may use any three-dimensional source materials identified in the folio you have selected.

You will be allowed up to 20 minutes after the examination to assemble your work on the maximum number of sheets ($2 \times$ A2 sheets).

This extension time is not to be used for producing examination work.

Note: Copying of drawings and/or photographs from your folio by means such as TRACING, LIGHT BOXES, DIGITAL CAMERAS and PHOTOCOPYING **will not be permitted during the examination**. This exclusion also includes the use of computers and images and information copied from folios and stored on disk and/or CD.

Select **either** SECTION A **or** SECTION B.

SECTION A

Expressive Activity

Task

You should produce practical work which demonstrates your ability to develop and/or refine work carried out in your Expressive folio. This could take the form of new and further developments from your stimulus and might include extending ideas leading to alternative outcome(s) not fully explored within the work of your folio.

Remember that work produced for this Assignment should relate directly to your EXPRESSIVE folio theme and must develop, not copy, work already done. Further investigative work, such as analytical drawing, is not appropriate in this Assignment.

The following suggestions are provided to help you get started:

- produce work based on the stimulus or sources used by you but not fully explored in the work of your Expressive folio

- produce work which emphasises a different style or approach to your chosen theme.

Work should be on a maximum of **two** A2 sheets or equivalent three-dimensional work. You may use any suitable media, materials or process.

SECTION B

Design Activity

Task

You should produce practical work which demonstrates an alternative approach or approaches to work carried out in your Design folio. This could take the form of new and further developments from your brief and might include extending Design ideas not fully explored within the work of your folio.

Remember that work produced for this Assignment should relate to your DESIGN brief and Design folio and must develop, not copy, work already done. Further investigative work, such as analytical drawing, is not appropriate in this Assignment.

The following suggestions are provided to help you get started:

• develop Design ideas which you considered but did not fully explore in the work of your Design folio

• reconsider your solution and suggest further modifications and/or changes to improve it.

Work should be on a maximum of **two** A2 sheets or equivalent three-dimensional work. You may use any suitable media, materials or process.

[END OF QUESTION PAPER]

[BLANK PAGE]

X003/302

NATIONAL QUALIFICATIONS 2006	THURSDAY, 25 MAY 1.00PM – 3.00PM	**ART AND DESIGN** HIGHER Paper 2

There are **two** sections to this paper, Section 1—Art Studies; and Section 2—Design Studies.

Each section is worth 40 marks.

Candidates should attempt questions as follows:

In SECTION 1 answer **ONE full question** (parts (*a*) and (*b*)) and **ONE part (*a*) only** of any other question

and

In SECTION 2 answer **ONE full question** (parts (*a*) and (*b*)) and **ONE part (*a*) only** of any other question.

You may use sketches to illustrate your answers.

SECTION 1—ART STUDIES

Instructions

Answer **ONE full question**, (parts (*a*) and (*b*)), and **ONE part (*a*) only** of any other question.

John Bellany   *My Father* (1966) oil on board (122 × 91·5 cm)

Marks

1.   Portraiture

(*a*)   Discuss the methods used by the artist to reveal aspects of his father's character to us. Comment on composition, use of visual elements and handling of paint. Explain your personal reaction to this portrait.   **10**

(*b*)   Discuss contrasting approaches to portraiture by **two** artists from different movements or periods. Comment on their choice of subjects, styles and working methods. Explain why you consider your artists to be important.   **20**

SECTION 1—ART STUDIES (continued)

Sebastião Salgado, *Dispute between Serra Pelada gold mine workers and military police*,
Brazil, 1986

Marks

2. **Figure Composition**

(*a*) Discuss the composition of this photograph. Comment on the relationships between the figures. How successfully does the photograph capture the tension of the situation? **10**

(*b*) Discuss the use of the human figure as subject matter. Refer to the work of **two** artists from different movements or periods. Compare the working methods and styles of these artists and comment on their success and importance. **20**

[Turn over

SECTION 1—ART STUDIES (continued)

Henri Matisse *Goldfish and Palette* (1914) oil on canvas (146 × 112 cm)

Marks

3. Still Life

(*a*) Discuss how **two or more** of the following contribute to the impact of this painting:

composition;   *abstraction;*   *visual elements;*   *media handling.*

What thoughts or feelings are communicated to you when you view this painting?   **10**

(*b*) Discuss examples of still life by **two** artists from different movements or periods. Comment on their choice of subject matter, working methods and style. Explain why you consider them to be influential artists.   **20**

SECTION 1—ART STUDIES (continued)

Christo and Jeanne-Claude *Wrapped Coast* (1969). The coastline of Little Bay, Australia, wrapped in fabric and rope. © Christo 1969

Marks

4. Natural Environment

(*a*) Discuss the methods used by the artists to create this example of Land Art[1]. Comment on the use of materials, scale and choice of site. Explain your personal reaction to this work.

10

(*b*) Discuss the working methods of **two** artists from different movements or periods who have taken inspiration from the natural environment. Referring to examples, comment on their different approaches and styles. Explain why you consider them to be important artists.

20

[1]*Land Art*—a type of art in which the artist uses actual land, earth and stones combined with other objects.

[Turn over

SECTION 1—ART STUDIES (continued)

David Mach *Here to Stay* (1990) Installation[1] using recycled newspapers.

[1]*Installation*—a form of art in which objects, images, words and video are often used together in a gallery or other space to communicate the artist's message. This installation has been created from 180 tons of surplus daily newspapers.

Marks

5. Built Environment

(a) What is your opinion of this installation? In your answer comment on methods of construction, scale and choice of materials. **10**

(b) Discuss the working methods of **two** artists from different movements or periods. Referring to examples within the theme of the Built Environment, comment on their choice of subject matter and differences in approach. Explain how the examples are typical of their styles. **20**

SECTION 1—ART STUDIES (continued)

Goya   *Colossus*[1] (1808–1812) oil on canvas (116 × 105 cm)

[1]*Colossus*—larger than life figure

Marks

6. Fantasy and Imagination

(a) Discuss the composition of this painting.   Comment on the use of visual elements and the methods used by the artist to communicate a feeling of terror.   What are your personal thoughts about this work?   **10**

(b) Discuss **two** artists from different movements or periods whose work within this theme interests you.   Referring to examples, discuss the methods used by the artists to communicate their ideas.   Explain why you consider them to be influential artists.   **20**

[Turn over

Instructions

Answer **ONE full question**, (parts (*a*) and (*b*)), and **ONE part (*a*) only** of any other question.

Travel poster by Alphons Mucha (1897)

Marks

7. Graphic Design

(*a*) Discuss the effectiveness of this poster design with particular reference to its imagery, layout and use of colour. In your opinion, how does this poster differ from modern posters?

10

(*b*) Choose **two** graphic designers working in different periods or styles and compare their methods of visual communication. Identify key aspects of their work and state why they are regarded as important designers.

20

SECTION 2—DESIGN STUDIES (continued)

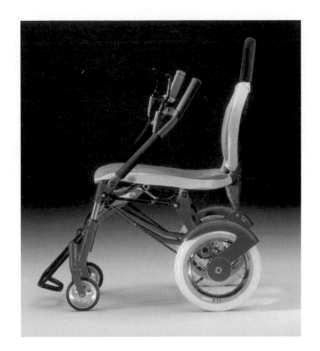
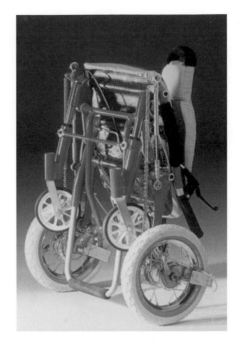

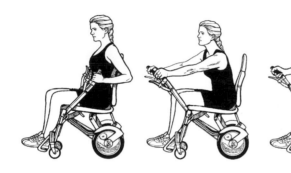

moving forward   *turning*

New Move Wheelchair designed by Douglas Clarkson (1994). *The chair is lightweight, foldable and powered by the user moving the handle bars in a forward/backward movement.*

Marks

8. Product Design

(*a*) Style, function and target market are important considerations in the development of a design concept. Comment on each of these in relation to Douglas Clarkson's wheelchair design. In your opinion how successful is the design and why?

10

(*b*) Select **two** designers working in different periods or styles. With reference to examples of their work, discuss how they have contributed to the development of everyday products. Which of the **two** do you consider to be the more important designer and why?

20

[Turn over

SECTION 2—DESIGN STUDIES (continued)

Dance Club designed by Graven Images (1999)

Marks

9. Interior Design

(*a*) Identify the key design issues that have been considered in the designing of this contemporary interior. With particular reference to the use of lighting and space, consider how effective the designers' ideas are. **10**

(*b*) Select **two** interior designers who work in different periods or styles and comment on their importance. Compare their approaches to the designing of interiors by referring to their use of at least **two** of the following: lighting, materials, space, colour, form, influences. **20**

SECTION 2—DESIGN STUDIES (continued)

Lloyds Building, London designed by architect Richard Rogers (1986)

Marks

10. Environmental/Architectural Design

(a) How has Richard Rogers's use of materials, forms and structures made this building stand out from those in its immediate surroundings? Do you consider that his vision for this contemporary building has been successful? Give reasons for your answer.

10

(b) Select **two** architectural/environmental designers working in different periods. With reference to at least **two** examples of their work, show how their use of materials and working methods have contributed to the development of architecture. Explain why they are considered to be important designers.

20

SECTION 2—DESIGN STUDIES (continued)

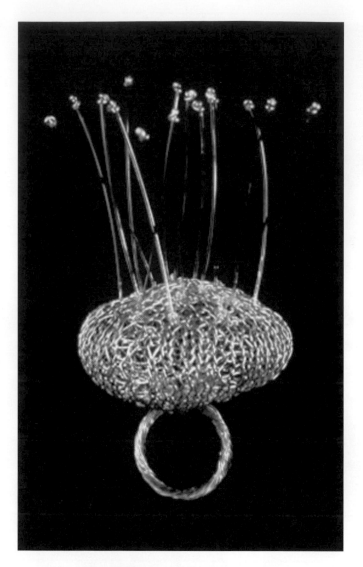 

Regeneration Ring, knitted nylon   *Thistle Ring*, woven nylon

Rings by Nora Fok (1999)

Marks

11. Jewellery Design

(a) Discuss Nora Fok's choice of materials, working methods and sources of inspiration for these jewellery pieces. Which target audience do you think that these pieces are aimed at, and how practical do you consider them to be as fashion accessories? Justify your answer.   **10**

(b) "Jewellery designers produce accessories which compliment the work of the fashion designer." Do you agree? Discuss this statement with reference to the work of **two** jewellery designers from different periods or styles. Explain their contribution to the development of jewellery.   **20**

SECTION 2—DESIGN STUDIES (continued)

Costume for *the Blue God* by Léon Bakst for the Ballet Russes,
Russian State ballet (1912)

Marks

12. Textile Design

(a) Discuss the ways in which Léon Bakst has used shape, pattern, colour and applied decoration to create this costume. How practical do you think the design is, and how might its appearance enhance the ballet production? **10**

(b) Refer to the work of **two** fashion and/or textile designers, working in different periods or styles. Show how they have experimented with new and/or unusual materials and working methods in the development of fashion and/or textile design. Explain why they have been influential in this field of design. **20**

[END OF QUESTION PAPER]

[BLANK PAGE]

[BLANK PAGE]

[BLANK PAGE]

[BLANK PAGE]

[BLANK PAGE]

Official SQA Past Papers: Higher Art & Design 2006

[BLANK PAGE]

Acknowledgements

Leckie & Leckie is grateful to the copyright holders, as credited, for permission to use their material.

Object: Breakfast in Fur Meret by Oppenheim: © DACS 2005, © Photo SCALA, Florence, DIGITAL IMAGE © 2003 The Museum of Modern Art/Scala, Florence (2003 P2 Q3);

Norham Castle Sunrise by J.M.W. Turner, © Tate, London 2006 (2003 P2 Q4);

A Manufacturing Town by L.S. Lowry, ©The Lowry Estate (2003 P2 Q5);

I and the Village by Marc Chagall: © ADAGP, Paris and DACS, London 2005, © Photo SCALA, Florence, DIGITAL IMAGE © 2003 The Museum of Modern Art/Scala, Florence (2003 P2 Q6);

The Woodsawyers by Jean Francois Millet, © V&A Images, The Victoria & Albert Museum, London (2004 P2 Q2);

Storm in the Jungle by Edward Burra: © The Estate of Edward Burra/V&A Images, The Victoria & Albert Museum, London (2004 P2 Q6);

Diego on My Mind (Self-Portrait as Tehuana Indian) by Frido Kahlo © 2006 Banco de México Diego Rivera & Frida Kahlo Museums Trust. Av. Cinco de Mayo No. 2, Col. Centro, Del. Cuauhtémoc 06059, México, D.F. (2005 P2 Q1);

The Dance by Paul Rego, © Tate, London 2006/Paula Rego (2005 P2 Q2);

The Wheatfield by Raol Duffy © ADAGP, Paris and DACS, London 2005/Tate, London 2006 (2005 P2 Q4);

Market Church at Evening by Lyonel Feininger © DACS, London 2005 (2005 P2 Q5);

My Father by John Bellamy © National Galleries of Scotland/The Bridgeman Art Library (2006 P2 Q1);

Dispute between Serra Pelada gold mine workers and military police by Sebastião Salgado © nb pictures (2006 P2 Q2);

Goldfish and Palette by Henri Matisse. DIGITAL IMAGE © 2006 The Museum of Modern Art/Scala, Florence (2006 P2 Q3);

Dance Club by Graven Images © Keith Hunter/Arcblue (2006 P2 Q9);

Lloyds Building, London © Life File Photographic Library (2006 P2 Q10).

The following companies/individuals have very generously given permission to reproduce their copyright material free of charge:

The Bridesmaid by John Everett Millais,© Fitzwilliam Museum, Cambridge. (2003 P2 Q1);

The Last Supper in Footdee by Joyce Cairns, © Joyce Cairns (2003 P2 Q2);

IBM Poster by Paul Rand: Reprinted with permission © 1981 by International Business Machines Corporation. (2003 P2 Q7);

Nokia Mobile Phone, © Nokia (2003 P2 Q8);

Chiat Day Office by Gaetano Pesco, © Chiat Day (2003 P2 Q9);

GSA Photos by Taschen Köln, © Anthony Oliver (2003 P2 Q10);

Brooches of Coloured Tears by Wendy Ramshaw, © Bob Cramp (2003 P2 Q11);

Interior at Paddington by Lucian Freud © Lucian Freud (2004 P2 Q1);

Untitled (House) by Rachel Whiteread. Commissioned by Artangel, sponsored by Beck's. Courtesy Gagosian Gallery (2004 P2 Q5);

Reaper Man by Josh Kirby, reproduced by permission of The Random House Group (2004 P2 Q7);

Swiss Army Knife © Victorinox (2004 P2 Q8);

JetBlue Airways–Airbus A320-232 © JetBlue Airways (2004 P2 Q9);

Belt Buckle in silver and enamel by Jessie M King, © Tadema Gallery (2004 P2 Q11);

Still Life with Vase of Hydrangeas and Ranunculus by Henri Fantin-Latour © Toledo Museum of Art (2005 P2 Q3);

Leviathan Elegy by Will Maclean © Will Maclean (2005 P2 Q6);

Scoot Foldable Scooter by Fuseproject © Fuseproject (2005 P2 Q8);

Domestic Interior by Philip Webb © The Quarto Group Inc. (2005 P2 Q9);

Clear Channel Adshel by Enthoven Associates © Enthoven Associates (2005 P2 Q10);

Wrapped Coast by Christo and Jeanne-Claude © Christo 1969 (2006 P2 Q4);

Here to Stay by David Mach © Alan Wylie/Tramway (2006 P2 Q5);

Rings by Nora Fok © Crafts Council (2006 P2 Q11);

Costume for the Blue God by Léon Bakst © National Gallery of Australia (2006 P2 Q12).

Pocket answer section for
SQA Higher Art & Design
2003–2006

Published by Leckie & Leckie Ltd, 3rd Floor, 4 Queen Street, Edinburgh EH2 1JE
tel: 0131 220 6831, fax: 0131 225 9987, enquiries@leckieandleckie.co.uk, www.leckieandleckie.co.uk

Higher Art & Design
2003 Paper 1

Assessment Criteria For Expressive Folios

The folio should identify a personal theme and show appropriate investigation, with the development of visual ideas / images leading to an expressive outcome which communicates ideas or feelings related to the theme.

Expected performance at mark range 80 – 100

For the **Investigation** stage, the candidate should demonstrate:

- ability to identify fertile sources of study relevant to the theme
- high quality perceptive, analytical drawings from direct observation
- skill in at least two different media.

For the **Development** stage, the candidate should demonstrate:

- ability to creatively explore a minimum of two visual ideas
- ability to select and refine images
- control and sensitivity in the handling of materials.

For the **Outcome** stage, the candidate should demonstrate:

- ability to communicate personal ideas / feelings through a finished piece of artwork
- confident and competent use of visual elements
- refined use in media handling
- a clear awareness of aesthetic qualities.

Expected performance at mark range 64 – 79

For the **Investigation** stage, the candidate should demonstrate:

- ability to identify a suitable source of study, relevant to the theme
- ability to produce analytical drawing from direct observation
- some skill in the use of at least two different media.

For the **Development** stage, the candidate should demonstrate:

- ability to explore a minimum of two visual ideas
- ability to select and modify images
- skill in the handling of materials.

For the **Outcome** the candidate should demonstrate:

- ability to communicate personal ideas / feelings through a finished piece of artwork
- competence in the use of visual elements
- skill in media handling
- awareness of aesthetic qualities.

Expected performance at mark range 48 – 63

For the **Investigation** stage, the candidate should demonstrate:

- ability to identify a theme and sources of study
- ability to produce competent analytical drawings from direct observation
- use of at least two different media.

For the **Development** stage, the candidate should demonstrate:

- ability to produce a minimum of two visual ideas
- ability to select and modify one image
- competence in the handling of materials.

For the **Outcome** stage, the candidate should demonstrate:

- ability to communicate personal ideas / feelings through a finished piece of artwork
- competence in use of visual elements
- basic skills in media handling.

Practical Assignment: Expressive

The purpose of the Practical Assignment is to allow the candidate to demonstrate expressive skills and processes acquired during the course to further develop or refine work done in the related unit.

Higher Art & Design
2003 Paper 1 (cont.)

Work should be directly related to the theme identified in the Expressive Activity unit. Developments can be taken from any stage to the expressive folio but further investigation work is not appropriate here.

If drawing is used in the Practical Assignment it should be expressive / interpretive rather than observational in character.

Marks will be allocated as follows:

- clear integration with Expressive folio
- further creative / imaginative development of the theme
- creative and skilful use of the visual elements
- effectiveness of communication.

Assessment Criteria For Design Folios

Evidence is required for each of the four stages of the design process and it should be noted that it is the candidate's understanding of, and response to, the brief and design process which will determine overall performance.

At all levels of performance, the folio should clearly identify a design problem, evidence of market research of solutions to the same problem, show a clear sense of direction and demonstrate a well integrated design problem-solving process. Irrelevant analytical drawing is not appropriate for the Research and Investigation sheets.

Expected performance at mark range 80 – 100

For the **Investigation and Research** stage of the folio, the candidate should:

- investigate and research a written design brief with awareness, depth and insight
- show evidence of exploration of the design context and any related sources
- show understanding of design issues.

For the **Development** stage of the folio, the candidate should:

- develop a minimum of two possibilities
- show creative use of materials, processes and concepts
- select and refine one idea.

The **Solution** stage of the folio should:

- be complete, skilfully executed, effective and appropriate to the brief.

The **Design Evaluation** should fully document the problem-solving process

Expected performance at mark range 64 – 79

For the **Investigation and Research** stage of the folio, the candidate should:

- investigate from a design brief showing understanding and awareness of the problem to be solved
- show evidence of exploration of the design context
- show understanding of design issues.

For the **Development** stage of the folio, the candidate should:

- develop a minimum of two potential ideas
- show skilful use of materials and good understanding of processes
- select and refine one idea.

The **Solution** stage of the folio should:

- be complete, well-executed and appropriate to the brief.

The **Design Evaluation** should document the problem-solving process

Expected performance at mark range 48 – 63

For the **Investigation and Research** stage of the folio, the candidate should:

- investigate from a design brief showing some understanding and awareness of the problem to be solved
- show investigation of the design context
- show awareness of a design issue.

For the **Development** stage of the folio, the candidate should:

- show competence in the use of materials and processes
- develop a minimum of two ideas
- select and develop one idea.

The **Solution** stage of the folio should:

- be complete, competently produced and appropriate to the brief.

The **Design Evaluation** should outline the problem-solving process

Practical Assignment: Design

The purpose of the Practical Assignment is to let the candidate demonstrate design skills related to the context and brief of the Design unit. Developments can be taken from any stage of the Design folio but further investigation work is not appropriate here.

Marks will be allocated as follows:

- clear links with the design folio and brief

- exploration of alternative possibilities and / or design solution arising from the brief

- the quality of flexible, creative problem-solving

- effectiveness of communication

Higher Art & Design
2003 Paper 2

1. (a) Comments about the division of the picture plane and the means by which the viewer's eye is taken to the focal point of the face will be rewarded. The tonal values within the work and Millais' use of high colour should be commented on. Fine detail and careful brushwork should also be noted. Personal opinions about Millais' portrayal of the bridesmaid may touch on symbolism within the piece and the action of passing wedding cake through the ring (a custom practised up to Victorian times).

    (b) A study of portraiture by artists from different movements or periods should be evident. Comments could be made about the artists' choice of subjects and the methods used to complete their work. References to associated movements and a discussion of how the selected artists influenced others will feature in a good answer.

2. (a) Analysis of this painting should include a discussion of at least two of the following – colour, line, distortion or perspective. Comments may be made relating to the rich complementary colour, strong incisive line, distortion of facial features and hands and the unusual viewpoint and its affect on perspective. Justified personal interpretations of the painting (perhaps referring to religious sources or suggestions of a celebration) will be rewarded.

    (b) Answers to this question should reveal a study of the figure compositions by two artists selected from different periods. Comments should be made on the differences and/or similarities in the artists' approaches to figure composition and their working methods. Answers that offer reasoned arguments to the importance of the selected artists will be rewarded.

3. (a) Comments about the choice of materials and how the piece was created should be made. Answers should include personal opinions of the piece as it challenges traditional still life in many ways: it is 3D; it is not painted; and it uses everyday items as media, creating a strange and provocative aesthetic. As such, the piece triggers associations which are far removed from many traditional still life works.

    (b) Comparisons of the work of two artists from different movements or periods should focus on choice of subject matter, styles and working methods. Justified personal opinions should be made about the selected artists' contribution to the theme of still life. This might include ways in which the artists have influenced others or how they have used new media or methods to produce examples.

Higher Art & Design
2003 Paper 2 (cont.)

4. (a) Discussion of the painting should comment on Turner's use of soft, subtle colour as well as his use of diffused, blurred shapes. Comments on media handling might point out his use of oil paint in an almost watercolour technique, applied in thin washes producing a glowing effect. Reasoned arguments for the success of the painting will be rewarded.

   (b) Responses to this question should be based in a study of two artists from different periods or movements. Comparisons of examples should explain similarities and/or differences in, for example, choice of subject, style and working methods. Justified personal opinions of the importance of the artists will be rewarded.

5. (a) Opinions about the success of this work should focus on Lowry's use of drab neutrals and brown – the use of dark tones against a light sky – contrasting shapes in the buildings and figures – depth created by tone and perspective. Comments made on colour, tone, shape and perspective will feature in a good answer.

   (b) Knowledge of the work within this theme by two artists from different movements or periods should be evident. Comments on their choice of subject matter are expected. The artists' working methods should be discussed. It may be important to explain whether the artists worked directly from observation or from sketches or photographic sources. Scale, media handling and use of visual elements should also be discussed. An explanation of the ways in which the artists have been influential would gain marks.

6. (a) Discussion of the methods used by Chagall might touch on his use of juxtaposed shapes, impossible, dream-like images, changes in scale, distorted colour and shape and references to childhood.

   (b) Responses to this question should be based on a study of two artists from different movements or periods whose work is based on fantasy and imagination. Reference should be made to examples of the artists' work which are typical of their style and which enable the candidate to discuss their methods and how they have communicated their ideas. Justified personal opinions about the artists' importance would be rewarded.

7. (a) Answers to this part of the question will focus on the restricted use of lettering/text combined with the simplified forms of the symbols, a typical 'less is more' approach, much favoured by Paul Rand. Reference to the design's simplicity, wit and modernist approach will be rewarded. Good responses will mention that the collaged appearance of the symbols set on a large expanse of black background delivers a striking image. Justified personal opinions regarding the use of the symbols and what they communicate will feature in a good answer.

   (b) Knowledge and understanding of the work of two designers from different periods or styles is looked for. Reference should be made to specific examples of their work and the designers' working methods, processes and distinctive styles should be discussed. An awareness of the important contribution made by the designers to corporate identity and marketing of products would gain marks.

8. (a) Comments could be made about the colour screen of the phone, its stereo radio, its polyphonic ring-tones, its MMS messaging service, its pre-installed games and its capability to support WAP navigation and Java Technology. Java Technology enables the user to personalise the applications in the telephone. Mention could be made of the phone's function of providing emergency contact in times of difficulty. Comments about the item's perceived target audience also its status as a desirable 'fashion accessory' will be rewarded.

   (b) Answers should show a genuine understanding of the role of the product designer, the importance of function and an awareness of appropriate client groups.

9. (a) Answers should note the distinctive colour scheme of this office space and comparisons may be made to similar work spaces. Comments could be made on the flexible work space this design provides, the rich and varied textures and materials used in its construction, and the bright, cheerful and homely atmosphere it creates.

   (b) Comparisons of examples of interiors by two designers from different periods or styles should discuss differences and similarities in the main features of their work such as the intended use, materials, furniture, fittings and the designers' use of colour and other visual elements in the space. Justified opinions about the importance of the designers in this area of design are expected and would gain marks.

10. (a) A good answer will mention the scale of the huge windows that dominate the north facing façade, allowing a uniform light to fill the studio spaces – an importat functional aim of the architect in this design. Reference to Mackintosh's familiar grid pattern in the window design and his extensive use of ironwork (balcony, weather vane, detailing on the windows and on the railings which incorporate typical Mackintosh techniques) will be rewarded. Comments should also be made about the inclusion of the curved forms that have been carefully integrated into the overall design of the building, contributing to its style and uniqueness. A uniform light within the studios, an ambience conductive to creative activity and a safe working environment would be among the important considerations for Mackintosh when designing this building.

(b) Knowledge and understanding of the work of two designers from different periods or with contrasting styles is required. Discussion of the main characteristics of their work should focus on materials used, form and the innovative nature of their designs. There should be a clear indication of the standing and importance of the designers in environmental design or architecture.

11. (a) Any justified opinion of how well the designer has captured the theme would gain marks. In stating their opinions, candidates should refer to the designer's use of materials, colour, shape and form. Any well-argued points about the functionality of the pieces would be rewarded.

(b) Knowledge and understanding of the work of two designers from different periods or different styles is looked for. An awareness of the importance of influences and visual stimuli in the development of jewellery designs should be evident in good answers. References should be made to specific examples of work which illustrate the points made. Additional marks would be gained for the justification of their position as influential jewellery designers.

12. (a) To gain good marks, reference should be made to at least two of the listed items. The applied detailing on the coat will obviously be a major discussion point and views about Schiaparelli's use of 'visual trickery' (her interest in surrealism is apparent here), her distinctive use of materials and her clever designing of the inage to 'fit' the female form will be rewarded. Justification of this designer's status in this field of design will feature in a good answer.

(b) Reference should be made to the work of two textile or fashion designers from different periods or styles. In particular, an awareness of how the designers create ideas that appeal to different client groups (male/female, young/old, celebrity/high street fashion, etc.) is looked for. Marks will be awarded for justification of the designers' status in this area of design.

Higher Art & Design
2004 Paper 1

Please refer to the answer guidelines given for Paper 1 2003 on pages 1-3.

Higher Art & Design
2004 Paper 2

SECTION 1: ART STUDIES

1. Portraiture

(a) A detailed analysis of this painting should include a reference to Freud's use of colour and the tonal values within the work. The window as a source of light should be mentioned. Any observations about the artist's use of other visual elements will be rewarded.

Candidates are also required to comment on any two of the following:-
- pose
- composition
- detail
- setting

Justified personal responses about what the artist is communicating to us will be rewarded.

(b) A study that incorporates a level of knowledge and understanding of portraiture by two artists from different movements or periods should be evident.
Comments in a good answer should reveal an understanding of their contrasting styles. This would be shown through discussion of subject matter, use of visual elements such as colour or tone, media handling and working methods. Answers that attempt to explain the importance of the artists in the history of portraiture will be rewarded.

2. Figure Composition

(a) A good answer will comment on the use of strong diagonals and the creation of the focal point on the workman.
Millet's use of strong tonal contrasts and complementary colour to create an atmosphere should also be discussed.
The poses of the figures and Millet's lively brushwork create a sense of action in the painting. These and other justified opinions of the painting will be rewarded.

(b) Answers should centre on a study of figure compositions by two artists from different movements or periods.
Knowledge of the methods used by artists to communicate their ideas should be evident. Responses that justify the importance of the artists' contribution to the art of figure composition will be rewarded.

3. Still Life

(a) In discussing Blackadder's composition answers should comment on two of the four suggested points from the question.
The flat use of space; the flowing lines and natural shapes of the subject matter; the free and painterly use of watercolour; the artist's use

3. (a) continued

of delicate colour and soft tones should be commented upon.
Justified, personal opinions will be rewarded.

(b) Comparisons of examples should reveal good knowledge and understanding of the work of two artists from different movements or periods. In doing so answers should either explain how typical the examples are of the artists' associated movements or how influential each artist has been regarding the development of still life as a subject.

4. Natural Environment

(a) Answers should include comments on the grandeur of the subject matter: the tall, majestic trees sweeping and rising towards us. Monet's use of colour to suggest the warmth of the sun and the spontaneity of his brushwork should also be commented upon.
Justified personal opinions of the success of the piece will be rewarded.

(b) Responses to this question should be based on a study of two artists from different movements or periods. A knowledge of the main characteristics of their work as well as their aims and objectives should be evident. Answers should discuss working methods, subject matter, choice of medium and use of visual elements. For example the Impressionists worked ouside and used bright colours applied with quick, light brushstrokes in an attempt to capture a moment in time.

5. Built Environment

(a) Reference to the commonplace nature of the subject should feature in a good answer. The scale of the piece and the technical difficulties of casting it should also be discussed.
Answers could also mention the monochromatic effect of casting the house in plaster and concrete. Comments could also be made about how the positive and negative shapes and forms add to the strange ghostly appearance of the piece.
Justified personal opinions of the piece will be rewarded.

(b) A study of the work of two artists from different movements or periods within the theme of the built environment should be evident.
Comments on choice of subject matter and working methods will be rewarded.
A well-developed answer will attempt to explain the extent of the artists' influence on others.

6. Fantasy and Imagination

(a) There are lots of opportunities to discuss the content of the painting. There is a wealth of weird and wonderful objects and creatures to write about.

In discussing the composition answers should make comment on Burra's use of colour, line and pattern.

Personal interpretations of the piece will be rewarded.

(b) Responses to this question should be based on a study of two artists' work, within this theme, from different movements or periods.

Answers should refer to examples of work and discuss the methods used by the artists to communicate their ideas as well as the aims and characteristics of their work.

Responses explain why the examples are typical of the artists' styles through discussing composition, choice of medium and use of visual elements.

SECTION 2: DESIGN STUDIES

7. Graphic Design

(a) All well justified opinions of this book jacket design will be rewarded. Comment on the strong illustrative imagery and how it attempts to explain the content of the book could be made. The effect on the overall layout of the design by the two blocks of text and the bar code should be commented upon. Reference to at least two of the stated design aspects should be made.

(b) A study of the work of two graphic designers from different periods or whose styles contrast should be evident in responses.

Comments should be made about the designers' approach to graphic design and particularly their use of techniques, imagery, lettering, layout, influences and their respective target markets.

Importantly, answers should strive to justify the importance of the two designers in the field of graphic design.

8. Product Design

(a) The original knife was designed on three principles, high quality, versatility and design excellence. A good answer should highlight these principles by referring to the compactness of the design, the materials it is made from, its readily identifiable appearance, its cost effectiveness and its versatile functional properties. Safety aspects and the social implications of carrying a knife may be raised as concerns.

All justified opinions should be rewarded.

8. continued

(b) Responses should reveal a good knowledge of product design in general. Answers should also demonstrate ability to understand, analyse and evaluate the intentions and ideas of two designers from different periods or styles. Justification of the designers' importance and recognition in this area of design will be rewarded.

9. Interior Design

(a) In discussing this interior, good answers would make particular reference to the repetitive appearance of the design. The subdued colour scheme, the storage compartments and television monitors, as well as the long narrow passageway should be commented upon. Passenger comfort and safety should feature as major aspects of a good answer.

All well argued points will be rewarded.

(b) Answers should demonstrate a clear awareness of the two designers selected for discussion. Knowledge of their working methods and style of design, as well as justification for their importance as interior designers, should be evident in the response. Detailed knowledge of at least one example of work by each designer must be stated in order for the answer to achieve a high mark.

10. Environmental/Architectural Design

(a) Comments about the integration of curved and rectangular forms, the subtle colour scheme resulting from the clever use of brick and sandstone and the interesting use of glass and galvanised metal to break up the mass of the structure will feature in a good answer. Comments about the artwork, which defines the entrance or gateway into the housing complex should also be made.

All justified opinions about the success of the design and how it might impact on the local community will gain marks

(b) Answers should reveal a good knowledge and awareness of the work of two designers/architects from different periods or styles. Comments about their work in terms of form (materials, style, influences) and function (fitness for purpose, influences, markets) will be rewarded. Additional marks will be gained where it has been shown that this work is influential in today's society.

11 Jewellery Design

(a) The rhythmical flowing lines and forms of Art Nouveau (the abstracted bird shapes have been adapted from a CR Mackintosh design) and the natural forms of the six blossoms should be commented upon. Good answers should include a short explanation of jewellery and silversmithing techniques in support of the justification of the piece as an item of jewellery. All justified comments made comparing it to contemporary buckles will be rewarded.

8 Official SQA Answers to Higher Art & Design

Higher Art & Design
2004 Paper 2 (cont.)

11. continued

(b) A good answer will show an understanding of the working methods of two designers from different periods or styles and will place their design processes in an historical context. At least two of the areas specified in the question must be used to illustrate and support the response. Answers should justify the importance of the two designers to gain maximum marks.

12. Textile Design

(a) There is much to discuss in this typical Miyake outfit of the period. The form and function should be addressed and all relevant comment regarding the variety of textural ideas, the different approaches used in constructing the elements of the outfit and the rhythmical movements sculpted around the body will be rewarded.
A good answer will notice that Miyake concentrates on the coexistence of the fabric and the body, which is linked by movement, and that he is involved with identifying the space between the body and the outfit. This would gain high marks.

(b) Responses to this question might include a demonstrated knowledge of fashion, costume design, fabric (printed/constructed), etc and answers would be expected to discuss, in some detail, specific examples of work by the selected designers. Full marks can only be achieved when responses attempt to justify the importance of the designers in the context of the development of textile design.

Higher Art & Design
Paper 1 2005

Please refer to the answers guidelines given for Paper 1 2003 on pages 1-3

Higher Art & Design
Paper 2 2005

SECTION 1: ART STUDIES

1. Portraiture

(a) A successful response to this question requires you to demonstrate analytical skills and combine them with justified opinions. References to Kahlo's use of fine detail particularly in the pattern of the head-dress should be made. Her use of soft, feminine colour and the importance of line should also be discussed. Any justified opinion about the balance between realism and imagination in the portrait would gain marks. The image of Diego on her forehead, the Tehuana costume and the tendrils should be discussed and compared to the otherwise realistic treatment of the portrait.

(b) Responses to this question should be based on a study of the work of two artists from different movements or periods. Explanations of the success of examples of portraiture may comment on choice of subject, use of visual elements, style and media handling.
An understanding of the importance of the artists in the development of portraiture is required to gain full marks.

2. Figure Composition

(a) You will be rewarded for making reference to the rhythmical, flowing composition of the painting. When you comment on Rego's methods in creating visual impact you should refer to the strange setting, the mix of age groups, strong tonal values and colour relationships. Any justified personal opinions of the painting will be rewarded.

(b) Responses should centre on a study of figure compositions by two artists from different movements or periods.
Methods used by the artists to create their work should be explained. This may include discussion of composition, media, subject matter and use of visual elements.
Explanations of how the examples referred to are typical of the artists' style or associated movement are expected, in order to gain full marks.

3. Still Life

(a) When you comment on the choice of subject matter make reference to the fresh appearance of the fruit and flowers and the delicate nature of the whole subject matter. The artist's arrangement of the objects to create a triangular composition should be mentioned. You should discuss the use of controlled brushwork and fine detail as well as the use of bright colour against a neutral background. You should also discuss the tonal values within the painting. Justified personal opinions of the painting are required to gain full marks.

3. continued

(b) In comparing examples of still life by two artists from different movements or periods, you should point out any similarities and/or differences in, for example, choice of subject matter, media handling and use of visual elements.
Discussion of the influence of the artists in the development of still life is required to gain full marks.

4. Natural Environment

(a) Discussion of Dufy's methods should include his use of thin washes of paint, the light touches of outline and the use of warm and cold colour to create perspective. His choice of rural subject matter should also be discussed. You will be rewarded for making justified personal opinions of the painting.

(b) A study of the work of two artists from different movements or periods within this theme should be evident in your response. Your answer should include comments about what the artists have communicated about the natural environment by discussing their choice of subject matter and working methods. An explanation of why the artists are considered important is required in order to gain full marks.

5. Built Environment

(a) Discussion of the artist's treatment of the scene should include comments upon his use of line to fragment the composition of the painting and his use of warm and cold colour. The contrasting tonal values should also be discussed.
Justified personal opinions of the painting will be rewarded.

(b) Responses to this question should reveal a good knowledge of the work of two artists from different movements or periods based on this theme.
Discussion of choice of subject and the artists' working methods should be expected and rewarded.

You are required to explain how typical the examples are of the artists' associated movements or styles before full marks are awarded.

6. Fantasy and Imagination

(a) Your discussion of the content of this example and the artist's method of presenting it should focus on Maclean's gathering together of found objects with others which he has made. The objects relate to whale fishing and may be seen as being presented in a manner which resembles museum cases. You may liken Maclean's presentation to words and phrases on pages of a huge book that may be opened and closed. In discussing the work you are required to comment on at least two of the following –

Higher Art & Design
Paper 2 2005 (cont.)

6. (a) continued

form, scale, materials, colour, composition. Any justified personal opinion and personal interpretation of the piece will be rewarded.

(b) Answers should reveal a good knowledge and understanding of the work of two artists from different movements or periods. In discussion of their work, you should comment on sources of inspiration and methods used by the artists to produce their work. This may include comments on their choice of media, use of visual elements and composition. An explanation of why the artists are considered important is required before full marks are awarded.

SECTION 2: DESIGN STUDIES

7. Graphic Design

(a) To gain high marks for this question you should include comment on imagery, colour and type. The strong illustrative layout with the girl's head in a landscape with a mysterious plume of smoke filling the sky should be discussed. The hovering wasp should be referred to. You should comment on the simple but effective use of text which lists the ten tracks of the CD. The titles will help you respond to the second part of the question about the band, their type of music and their target market. Any well-reasoned views will gain marks.

(b) It is important that you refer to at least two examples of graphic design (one from each designer) in your response to this question. At least two of the specified design aspects must be discussed but you may attempt more. To gain full marks you must explain why your chosen designers are considered to be important in the history and development of graphic design.

8. Product Design

(a) You would be expected to highlight as many of the following points as possible that would make this product a worthwhile purchase:

- Its portability
- It is manufactured from lightweight yet durable materials (carbon fibre and aluminium)
- It is a socially acceptable design idea, harmless to the environment and might be the answer to traffic congestion problems, especially in large cities
- It is easily maintained
- It is very easily stored and ideal for work places, town centre flats, compact living, etc.

Disadvantages might include the perception that it is a "fair-weather toy" and would require a major marketing exercise to establish its popularity in this country. All justified points and opinions will gain marks.

8. continued

(b) Your response to this question should reveal the study of the work of two product designers from different periods or styles. You should be able to show that the designers are aware of the needs of the marketplace and the opportunities it presents for their exploration and development of these needs, its problems, tastes and desires.

Issues relating to available technologies, materials, trends and manufacturing processes might be among a range of appropriate and relevant matters for discussion, and referring to specific examples of their work should highlight these.

To gain additional marks, you should show how these designers are regarded as important figures in the field of product design.

All justified opinions to this question should be rewarded appropriately.

9. Interior Design

(a) In your answer to this question you should concentrate on the "dated" look and vast space of this interior. The integration of period furniture, wood panelling, heavily patterned carpet, classical artwork on the walls, moulded high ceiling and large windows should all be discussed. In order to gain full marks you must make comparisons with domestic interiors of today. Any justified opinions, which concentrate on interior design issues, would be rewarded.

(b) Your answer to this question will be based on the study of the work of two interior designers from different periods or styles. As with all part (b) questions, your choice of designers will shape your answer but you must demonstrate an understanding of the designers' style, distinctive approach to working, use of materials and their unique and innovative response to trends and fashions. To gain full marks you must explain the importance of your designers within the sphere of interior design.

10. Environmental/Architectural Design

(a) In your answer you should discuss the following as important design considerations:
  - The choice of weather resistant materials that are sympathetic to the immediate environment. In this instance materials used include: UV-resistant, translucent polycarbonate roof, which has a reflective screen-printed finish for maximum illumination. Extruded aluminium profiles. Materials are graffiti-resistant.
  - The shelter has a refreshingly stylish, clean and unobtrusive quality, which suggests that its relationship with its immediate environment has been a priority for the design team.
  - The integrated telephone design will be flagged up as an important safety and "emergency" feature.
  - The screen, which displays contemporary advertising, adds vibrancy at street level and an exciting dimension to city living. It might also be suggested that it will provide income for essential maintenance of the structure.
  - It provides adequate shelter from the elements in a simple, stylish and comfortable manner.
  - Good, justified personal views about this "building" should gain extra marks.

(b) Answers that demonstrate a sound understanding of the two chosen designers by referring to examples of their work and specifically to the four listed design aspects should be well rewarded. You should also explain why the two designers are important in this field of design to gain additional marks.

11. Jewellery Design

(a) This contemporary approach to body adornment will provoke strong views about the practicality of the design and the choice of materials. You might have views about the hand pieces, for example, are they potential weapons? Who do you think would wear the example? On what occasion would it be worn? All justified personal opinions will rewarded.

(b) This question offers plenty of scope for an in depth discussion of the role of the jewellery designer. The main thrust of your response should focus on how your selected designers have "broken new ground" in their search for stylish and functional jewellery ideas. Reference to examples of their work is required. The listed design aspects provide you with topics for discussion. You must discuss at least two of them with reference to examples by your designers. Full marks can only be gained by explaining the influence your designers have had in the development of jewellery design.

12. Textile Design

(a) In your response to this question the following design issues should be discussed:
  - Safety – a prime aspect of this design.
  - Materials – Kevlar is a relatively new material, which has strength, flexibility and will allow the body to "breathe". It is also easy to cut, shape and join.
  - Style – the suit has been "fashioned" for function and aesthetic appeal. Candidates might make reference to the contrast in the colour of the piece, the applied design, which could have been inspired by the tread of a tyre or the vertebrae of the back, and which is placed at strategic points on the suit for maximum protection.
  - Cost – value for money is a vital consideration in all design and it can be assumed that the designer (Edward Harber) gave this his due consideration.
  - Target Market – this item is aimed at a restricted marketplace, which has implications for a number of important points. A limited market means that purchase costs are generally higher, repairs (which in this case could be fairly frequent) can be costly and inconvenient, and a "youngish" target market might wish to keep up with an ever-changing fashion scene by buying the latest styles. It has a strong, masculine identity.
  - All justified views regarding the suit, as a fashion item, should gain marks.

(b) This is a wide open question, which should encourage you to demonstrate your knowledge and understanding of this area of design. References to examples of work by two designers from different periods or styles are required. An explanation of the importance and influence of your chosen designers is looked for to gain full marks.

Higher Art & Design
Paper 1 2006

Please refer to the answer guidelines given for Paper 1 2003 on pages 1–3

Higher Art & Design
Paper 2 2006

SECTION 1: ART STUDIES

1. Portraiture

(a) From your studies you may know that Bellamy's father was a fisherman. In any case you should recognise the signs of a hardworking man. Comments about his large strong hands would gain marks. His weathered face and stern look should also be commented upon. The tattoo and rolled up cigarette may also suggest a typical working man of that era. Bellamy's father's gaze with no eye contact should be discussed. His overalls and working clothes should also be discussed and would gain marks. The triangular composition of the painting with the arms resting along the top of one of Bellamy's paintings should be discussed because this helps to create a focal point in the face. The inclusion of one of Bellamy's paintings may also be seen as symbolically significant. Comments about the use of earthy colour and strong tonal values would gain marks. Other visual elements may also be discussed. Bellamy's strong, direct brushwork particularly in his treatment of the texture of the skin should be discussed. Any justified personal opinion of the painting would be rewarded.

(b) Responses to this question should be based on a study of the contrasting work of two portrait artists from different movements or periods. Explanations of the differences on their choice of subjects, styles and working methods would be well rewarded.
A full answer to this part of the question would gain a maximum of 16 marks and a further 4 marks are available for the explanations of the importance of the artists in the development of portraiture.

2. Figure Composition

(a) Discussion of the composition of the photograph should explain how the central figures are framed to create a focal point in the policeman and mineworker. Comments on the strength of the mineworkers would gain marks. Their strength is seen in numbers and also in the stature of the central figure. Compare that strength to the considerably smaller policeman outnumbered completely by the workers. Any justified comment on the success the photograph has in capturing tension would be rewarded. The low viewpoint of the photographer contributes to the success, as does the use of monochrome. The overpowering strength of the central worker grabbing the rifle contributes greatly to the tension.

2. (b) Responses to this question should be based on a study of figure compositions by two artists from different movements or periods. Comparisons of examples of work by the artists are required. In doing so discussion of composition, media handling, use of visual elements and choice of subject matter would gain marks.

A total of 16 marks are available for the comparison and discussion and a further 4 marks are available for justified opinions on the success of the artists and their importance in the development of figure composition.

3. Still Life

(a) This question requires the candidate to comment on two or more listed aspects in an analysis of the painting. Comments on the flat, linear compression and how that produces a limited sense of space would gain marks. The degree of abstraction in the painting would be summed up by commenting on the reduction to basic shapes. Comments on visual elements should include the impact of the use if strong tonal values and the striking effect of a limited use of colour against neutrals. Comments on Matisse's free and spontaneous brushwork would also gain marks.

Any explanation of thoughts or feelings communicated by the painting would be rewarded.

(b) This is a straightforward question and should reveal a study of the work of two artists from different movements or periods. A good knowledge and understanding of the artists' choice of subject matter, media, handling and use of visual elements should be evident in responses.

Up to 16 marks are awarded for the first part of the question and a further 4 marks are available for explanations of the influence the artists have or had on the development of still life.

4. Natural Environment

(a) Discussion of this example of land art should centre around the combination of man made fabric with a natural rock formation. The scale of the work, which is obviously huge, should be commented upon. Reference to the human figures in the photograph would help explain the impact of scale. The artists' choice of such a dramatic coastline and the effect of covering it in thin cloth to partially change its appearance should be discussed.

Any fully explained personal reactions to the work would be rewarded.

4. (b) A study of the work of two artists from different movements or periods should be evident in a response to this question. Answers should reveal a good knowledge and understanding of the working methods of the artists. Differences and/or similarities in style and approach to work based on the natural environment should be discussed.

Up to 16 marks are available for this part of the question and a further 4 marks for an explanation of the importance of the artists in the development of this type of work.

5. Built Environment

(a) Any justified opinion of this work would be rewarded. Comments on the artist's method of construction and his need for assistance because of the scale of the work would also gain marks. Discuss the impact of the scale of the sculpture and comments on the re-use of surplus newspapers would gain marks.

(b) Responses to this question should reveal a good knowledge of the work, based on this theme, of two artists from different movements or periods.

Discussion of the artists' working methods should make reference to examples of work and comment on their choice of subject matter and differences in approach.

Up to 16 marks are available for this part of the question and another 4 marks are available when it is explained how the examples are typical of the artists' style.

6. Fantasy and Imagination

(a) An analysis of the composition of this painting should comment on the strong contrast in tonal values and the use of bright colour in a mostly neutral setting. Marks would also be gained by commenting on the huge naked figure with clenched fist rising through the clouds. The inclusion of such a figure obviously communicates terror. The fleeing people and animals are other means of suggesting terror. Any well explained personal thoughts about the painting would be rewarded.

(b) Answers to this question should reveal a good knowledge and understanding of the work of two artists from different movements or periods. Refer to examples of work by each artist and explain the methods used by them to communicate their ideas.

Up to 16 marks are available for the first part of the question and a further 4 weeks when it is explained why the artists are influential in the development of this type of work.

Higher Art & Design
Paper 2 2006 (cont.)

SECTION 2: DESIGN STUDIES

7. Graphic Design

(a) Responses to this question should highlight the strong illustrative approach and the flowing rhythmical qualities of the design layout. Comments about the stylisation of the plant forms contrasting with the naturalistic forms of the female figure would be rewarded. Comments about the style and position of lettering would also gain marks. Any opinions about the poster including the use of a female form to promote a message would be rewarded. Well-stated comparisons with contemporary poster designs would gain marks.

(b) The two designers must be working in different periods or their styles must be obviously contrasting and a good knowledge, understanding and awareness of their working methods should be evident in an answer to the question. Discussion of the designer's use of materials, imagery and techniques would be necessary.
Up to 16 marks are available for this and a further 4 marks are available for comments about the importance of the designers in the development of graphic design

8. Product Design

(a) An awareness of the "eye catching" properties of this wheelchair design would gain marks. Comments on its striking colour, wheel design, lack of sides and armrests and its distinctive handle bars/grips would be rewarded. Marks would also be given for any justified opinion about its operational capability as well as its adaptability for storage and transportation. Opinions about the product's target market would also gain marks.

(b) The question offers a wide range of possible responses. The list of everyday products is extensive but the designers studied will influence answers. It would be appropriate to write about new innovative products or the restyling and development of established products. Both approaches would be acceptable. Up to 16 marks are available and a further 4 marks when a clear understanding of the historical importance of the selected designers is stated.

9. Interior Design

(a) This type of space is familiar to most and strong personal opinions should be stated when answering. The lighting and screen features and otherwise minimalist treatment of the interior should be discussed. Safety issues should also be discussed and, as with all aspects of the question, well-stated personal opinions will be rewarded.

9. (b) This question focuses on important aspects of the interior design process and requires knowledge and understanding of the work of the two designers as it relates to the list of specific areas for discussion. A simple biographical answer will not gain high marks. Up to 16 marks are available for the first part of the question and a further 4 marks for comments on the designers' relevance and standing in this field of design.

10. Environmental/Architectural Design

(a) Comments on the building's physical presence in the cityscape with reference to scale and use of materials would be rewarded. The architect's decision to incorporate the building's services on the outside and how that creates a distinctive form and frees up internal space should be discussed. Comments on how the building integrates with others nearby and any well argued opinions would be rewarded.

(b) This question offers plenty scope to demonstrate knowledge and understanding of the work of two key figures in the history of architecture. Discussion of their unique contribution regarding the introduction of particular materials and working practices should gain up to 16 marks. A further 4 marks are available for discussion of their influence on the development of Environmental/Architectural Design.

11. Jewellery Design

(a) Discussion and explanation of Nora Fok's working methods and techniques would be rewarded. Comments on her source of inspiration in the natural environment and links to the organic forms in her jewellery would gain marks. Opinions regarding her choice of materials would also gain marks. Well-argued answers regarding the target audience and practicalities of wearing the items will be rewarded.

(b) This question requires a statement about the link between two areas of the fashion world and any well-justified opinions will gain marks. The choice of designers is important and good discussion depends on depth of study and awareness of the differing roles of jewellery designers.
Up to 16 marks are awarded for the first part of the question and a further 4 marks for an explanation of the importance of selected designers in their specialist areas.

12. Textile Design

(a) There is plenty to discuss in this design in terms of its immediate visual appeal. Bakst's use of materials, the costume's colour, pattern and symmetry of the design, as well as its simple, effective shape should be commented upon and a good answer would highlight the theatrical aspect of the costume design.

(b) Answers to this question should reveal an in depth knowledge of the work of two designers from different periods or styles. Responses may be in fashion design, costume design, printed textiles etc.
Up to 16 marks are available for the first part of the question and a further 4 marks for an explanation of the importance of the two designers within their specialist area.

Official SQA answers to 1-84372-433-2
2003–2006